It's Crossword Time 1

Test Your Vocabulary

It's Crossword Time 1

Peter Watcyn-Jones

Illustrated by Colin Mier

PENGUIN BOOKS

PENGUIN BOOKS

Published by the Penguin Group
Penguin Books Ltd, 27 Wrights Lane, London W8 5TZ, England
Penguin Books USA Inc., 375 Hudson Street, New York, New York 10014, USA
Penguin Books Australia Ltd, Ringwood, Victoria, Australia
Penguin Books Canada Ltd, 10 Alcorn Avenue, Toronto, Ontario, Canada M4V 3B2
Penguin Books (NZ) Ltd, 182–190 Wairau Road, Auckland 10, New Zealand

Penguin Books Ltd, Registered Offices: Harmondsworth, Middlesex, England

Test Your Vocabulary: It's Crossword Time 1 published by Penguin Books 1992
10 9 8 7 6 5 4

Illustrations by Colin Mier
Designed by Karen Osborne

Set in Century Schoolbook
Printed in England by Clays Ltd, St Ives plc

Contents

Numbers

Complete the crossword by filling in the missing numbers. (See example)

Across →

2 He was born in 1912 and died in 1975. He was ....-.................... years old when he died. (5,5)

6 There are .... days in a week. (5)

8 Children in Britain start school at the age of .... (4)

10 We have .... fingers and two thumbs. (5)

11 October is the .... month of the year. (5)

13 A square has .... sides. (4)

14 He won the first point in the tennis match, so the score was ....–0. (7)

16 There are .... months in a year. (6)

20 .... is XIV in Roman numerals. (8)

Down ↓

1 Christmas Day is on December the twenty-.................... (5)

3 Many people think this number is unlucky. (8)

4 There are .... players in a football team. (6)

5 There are three .... and sixty-five days in a year. (7)

7 9 + 7=.................... (7)

9 100 × 100=.................... (8)

12 There are .... days in September. (6)

15 100 ÷ 5=.................... (6)

17 In Britain and most other European countries, you can vote at the age of .... (8)

18 We are living in the .... century. (9)

19 A triangle has .... sides. (5)

Picture crossword: food and drink

Look at the drawings and complete the crossword.

Across →

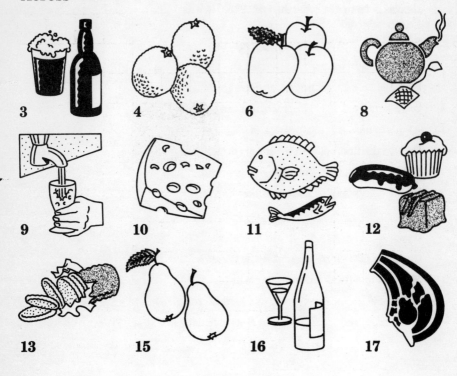

3   4   6   8

9   10   11   12

13   15   16   17

Down ↓

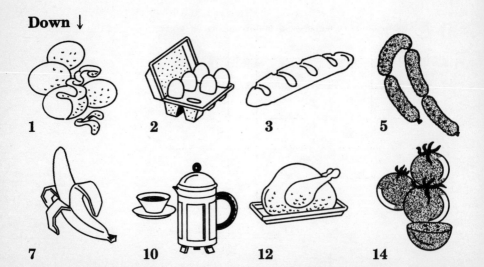

1   2   3   5

7   10   12   14

3 Opposites: adjectives

Complete the crossword by finding a word that is opposite in meaning to each of the adjectives.

Across →		**Down ↓**	
1	expensive (5)	2	sad (5)
7	dead (5)	3	late (5)
9	rich (4)	4	cruel (4)
10	beautiful (4)	5	heavy (5)
11	clean (5)	6	hot (4)
13	dry (3)	8	full (5)
14	difficult (4)	12	fat (4)
16	right (5)	15	hard (4)
19	big (5)	16	strong (4)
21	young (3)	17	bad (4)
22	quick (4)	18	open (6)
23	thin (5)	19	tall (5)
		20	high (3)

Irregular verbs   1

Complete the crossword by filling in the correct part of each verb (infinitive or past tense) in the table. (See example)

Across→

Infinitive	Past tense
bring	*2 Across (7)*
5 Across (5)	broke
teach	*6 Across (6)*
speak	*8 Across (5)*
carry	*10 Across (7)*
meet	*12 Across (3)*
hear	*14 Across (5)*
sell	*15 Across (4)*
get	*17 Across (3)*
18 Across (3)	saw

Down ↓

Infinitive	Past tense
buy	*1 Down (6)*
3 Down (5)	wrote
be	*4 Down (3)*
think	*7 Down (7)*
sit	*8 Down (3)*
say	*9 Down (4)*
do	*11 Down (3)*
13 Down (4)	fell
sleep	*15 Down (5)*
lose	*16 Down (4)*

Which country is it?

Read the information below and complete the crossword.
Each word is a country.

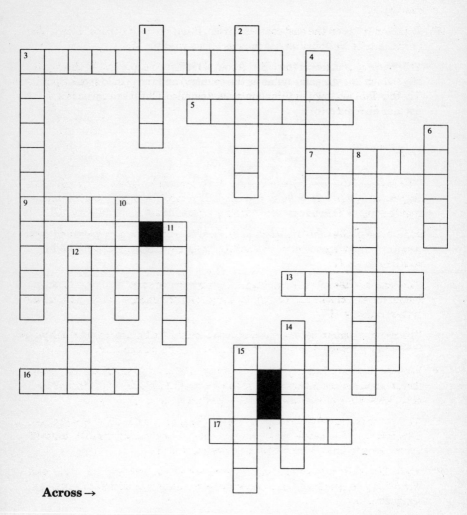

Across →

3 This country is in the Middle East. It is a very large country with lots of oil. It has a famous city called Mecca. (5,6)

5 Another name for this country is the Netherlands. It is famous for flowers (tulips), canals and diamonds. (7)

7 In this country they speak both French and English. Ice hockey is the national sport. It is very cold in winter and the capital city is Ottawa. (6)

9 This is a very large country which had a revolution in 1917. Vodka is the national drink and famous composers, e.g. Tchaikovsky and Prokofiev were born here. The capital city is famous for its Red Square. (6)

12 This country is famous for flamenco music and bullfighting. It is also very popular with tourists. One of its most famous cities is Barcelona. (5)

13 Pope John Paul II, Chopin and Lech Walesa were born in this country. The zloty is the currency and one of the most famous towns is Gdansk. (6)

15 Before October 1990 this country was two countries. They are very good at football and athletics. Beethoven, Bach and Boris Becker were born in this country. (7)

16 This country is on the east coast of Africa. It used to be a British colony. The capital city is Nairobi and it is famous for its wildlife. (5)

17 This country is south of the USA. About 20 million people live in the capital city (which has the same name as the country) and the people speak Spanish. Another famous town in this country is Acapulco. Chilli con carne is a popular dish here. (6)

Down ↓

1 This is one of the countries of Britain. Only two million people live here but they have their own language as well as English. The actor Richard Burton and the singer Tom Jones were born here. Cardiff is the capital city. (5)

2 This is one of the countries of Scandinavia. It is very cold in winter and most people like having a sauna. It is next to Russia and the composer Sibelius was born here. (7)

3 This country has lots of mountains. It is not very big and it is famous for its banks, cuckoo clocks and chocolate. They speak French, German and Italian in this country. (11)

4 This is a very small country in southern Europe. Its Prince married a famous Hollywood actress. It is famous for low taxes and its casino. (6)

6 This country is not very big and is a group of islands. It is famous for making cars, computers, cameras, etc. It is sometimes called 'the land of the rising sun'. It has an emperor and the national drink is saki. (5)

8 This country has two islands. They speak English here but it is a long way from Britain. The people who lived here first are called Maoris. The national sport is rugby and the capital city is Wellington. (3,7)

10 Many famous opera singers and painters were born here, e.g. Pavarotti and Michelangelo. Football is the national sport and typical dishes are pizza and spaghetti. (5)

11 This country has a very large population. Until the 1950s it was part of the British Empire. There are elephants and tigers here and curry is a popular dish. (5)

12 The film director Ingmar Bergman was born in this country. So were Björn Borg and Stefan Edberg. Volvo cars are also made here and many of the people are tall and blond with blue eyes. (6)

14 This country is in South America. It has a very good football team. It also has a famous carnival and it is from this country that we get the samba. (6)

15 This is a popular country with tourists. It has lots of small islands and has a warm climate. The Olympic Games started here. The national drink is ouzo and the national musical instrument is the bazouki. (6)

6 Dialogues

Complete the crossword by filling in the missing words from the dialogues below.

Across →

3 A: How .... are you? (3)
  B: I'm thirty-five.

4 A: .... train are you catching? (5)
  B: The 7.45. It goes from platform 11.

5 A: Would you close the door, ...? (6)
    B: Yes, certainly.

10 A: Hello, John. How are you?
     B: I'm fine, ... And you? (6)
     A: Very well, thank you.

12 A: David, this is Cathy Smith.
     B: .... Cathy. Pleased to meet you. (5)

13 A: How .... is it to London from here? (3)
     B: About 60 miles.

14 A: .... do you come from? (5)
     B: Italy. I was born in Rome.

15 A: How much .... this book cost? (4)
     B: £10.50.

17 A: I'm .... I'm late. (5)
     B: That's all right.

18 A: .... does the film start? (4)
     B: At 7.30, I think.

Down ↓

1 A: ....me, is this Green Street? (6)
    B: Yes, that's right.

2 A: I've just got married.
    B: Have you really? ....! (15)

6 A: I'm taking my driving test tomorrow.
    B: Well, good ....! (4)
    A: Thanks. I'll need it.

7 A: .... do you do? (4)
    B: I'm a teacher.

8 A: How .... are you? (4)
    B: About 1 metre 80 centimetres.

9 A: I'm thirty-five and my husband is thirty.
    B: So your husband is five years .... than you. (7)
    A: Yes, that's right.

11 A: I'd like a pair of shoes, please.
     B: Certainly. What .... do you take? (4)
     A: 10 or 10½.

12 A: .... a nice weekend! (4)
     B: Thank you. The same to you.

16 A: What time do you usually get up in the ....? (7)
     B: At 7 o'clock.

18 A: .... pen is this? (5)
     B: It's mine.

Prepositions

Complete the crossword by looking at the drawings and filling in the missing words. (See example)

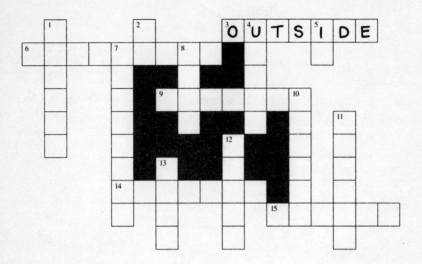

Across →

3 There's a bus stop .... the pub. (7)

6 She is standing .... the mirror. (2,5,2)

9 The bank is .... the post office and the restaurant. (7)

14 The postman pushed the letter .... the letter box. (7)

15 The library is at the .... of Green Street and London Road. (6)

Down ↓

1 The bird is
.... the cage. (6)

2 The keys are
.... the table. (2)

4 The cat is asleep
.... the bed. (5)

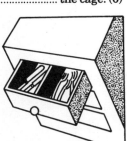

5 The knives and
forks are ....
the drawer. (2)

7 The police station is
.... the garage.
(8)

8 The horse is
jumping ....
the fence. (4)

10 The travel agency
is .... the
bookshop. (4,2)

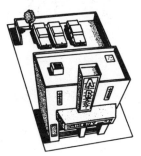

11 There's a car park
.... the cinema.
(6)

12 The coffee is on
the top shelf — on the
.... (5)

13 It is 50 miles ....
Cambridge to London. (4)

19

Picture crossword: parts of the body

Look at the drawings and complete the crossword.

A = Across →
D = Down ↓

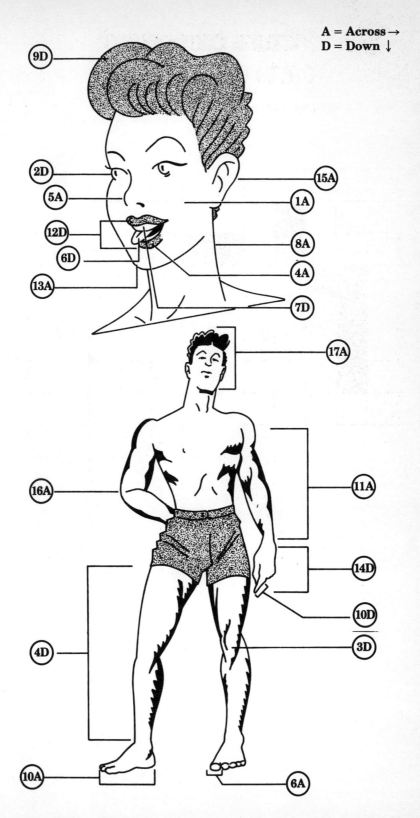

What's the job?

Read the definitions and complete the crossword. Each of the missing words is a type of job.

Across →

3   A .... is someone who sells bread and cakes. (5)

6   A .... is someone you go to when you are ill. (6)

7   A .... is someone who looks after a garden. (8)

9   An .... is a woman who acts in plays and films. (7)

10   A .... is someone who makes things (tables, chairs, etc.) out of wood. (9)

13   A .... is someone who works in a school. (7)

14   An .... is someone who paints pictures. (6)

17   A .... is someone who writes articles for a newspaper. (10)

19   A .... is someone who serves in a shop. (4,9)

Down ↓

1   A .... is someone who works on a boat. (6)

2   A .... is someone who cleans windows. (6,7)

4   A .... is someone who cooks in a restaurant. (4)

5   A .... is someone you call if your house is on fire. (7)

8   A .... is someone who works in a library. (9)

10   A .... is someone who repairs cars. (3,8)

11   A .... wears a uniform. You call this person if someone robs you. (9)

12   A .... is someone you go to when you have toothache. (7)

15   An .... is someone who tests people's eyes. You can also go to him or her if you want a new pair of glasses. (8)

16   A .... is someone who delivers letters to your house. (7)

18   A .... is someone who looks after you when you are in hospital. (5)

10 Opposites: verbs

Complete the crossword by finding a word that is opposite in meaning to each of the verbs.

Across →	Down ↓
1 stop (5)	1 buy (4)
2 open (5)	2 go (4)
4 find (4)	3 laugh (3)
6 remember (6)	5 whisper (5)
9 pull (4)	6 start (6)
12 teach (5)	7 bring (4)
13 ask (6)	8 lose, e.g. a race (3)
15 live (3)	10 love (4)
	11 borrow (4)
	14 arrive (5)

11 A family tree

Look at the drawing of the family tree. Read the text and fill in the missing words in the crossword.

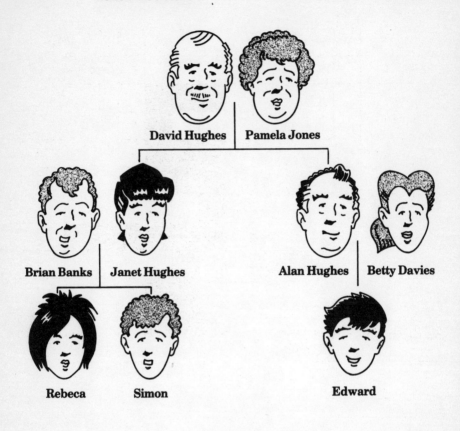

David Hughes   Pamela Jones

Brian Banks   Janet Hughes   Alan Hughes   Betty Davies

Rebeca   Simon   Edward

David and Pamela got married in 1950. David is Pamela's ....(4 Down) and Pamela is David's ....(8 Across). They have two ....(6 Down) – Janet and Alan. Janet is their ....(1 Down) and Alan is their .... (5 Across).

Edward's ....(9 Across) are called Betty and Alan. Betty is Edward's ....(7 Down) and Alan is his ....(11 Across). He also has an ....(14 Across) called Brian and an ....(12 Down) called Janet.

Rebecca is Simon's ....(15 Across) and Simon is Rebecca's .... (2 Down). Edward is their ....(10 Down). Rebecca, Simon and Edward are David and Pamela's ....(3 Across).

Rebecca is Betty and Alan's ....(13 Down) and Simon is their ....(16 Across).

Irregular verbs   2

Complete the crossword by filling in the correct part of each verb (infinitive or past tense) in the table.

Infinitive	Past tense
sing	*1 Across (4)*
2 Across (5)	built
4 Across (3)	ran
give	*6 Across (4)*
break	*7 Across (5)*
8 Across (6)	froze
catch	*9 Across (6)*
take	*12 Across (4)*
fly	*13 Across (4)*
go	*16 Across (4)*

Infinitive	Past tense
cut	*17 Across (3)*
1 Down (4)	swam
bite	*2 Down (3)*
drink	*3 Down (5)*
understand	*5 Down (10)*
7 Down (6)	became
10 Down (4)	hid
11 Down (4)	made
leave	*14 Down (4)*
keep	*15 Down (4)*

What's the word? 1

Read the sentences and complete the crossword. (See example)

Across →

2 It's black. You put it on a fire. It rhymes with **hole**. (4)

3 You can buy this at a post office. It rhymes with **lamp**. (5)

5 If you have one of these you shouldn't get lost. It rhymes with **cap**. (3)

8 A part of the body. It rhymes with **bed**. (4)

9 You use this when you make bread and cakes. It rhymes with **hour**. (5)

11 You live in it. It rhymes with **mouse**. (5)

13 A colour. It rhymes with **town**. (5)

15 A number. It rhymes with **wait**. (5)

17 The opposite of early. It rhymes with **hate**. (4)

18 In Britain a hundred pence make one of these. It rhymes with **round**. (5)

20 A popular drink. It rhymes with **toffee**. (6)

21 It's white and you see it in the winter. It rhymes with **know**. (4)

Down ↓

1 You might become this if you eat too many chocolates and cream cakes. It rhymes with **hat**. (3)

2 You can use this if your hair is untidy. It rhymes with **home**. (4)

4 A favourite drink in Britain. It rhymes with **sea**. (3)

5 A planet. It rhymes with **cars**. (4)

6 A fruit. It rhymes with **teach**. (5)

7 You sit on it. It rhymes with **hair**. (5)

9 Someone you like and can go to if you need help. It rhymes with **end**. (6)

10 You get this from a chicken. It rhymes with **leg**. (3)

12 Something men do every day – but not men with beards! It rhymes with **wave**. (5)

13 You borrow this from a library. It rhymes with **cook**. (4)

14 A door is usually made of this. It rhymes with **good**. (4)

16 A direction. It rhymes with **nest**. (4)

19 It's very hot. It rhymes with **bun**. (3)

20 A farm animal. It rhymes with **now**. (3)

Which verb?

Complete the crossword by filling in the missing verbs in the sentences.
(See example)

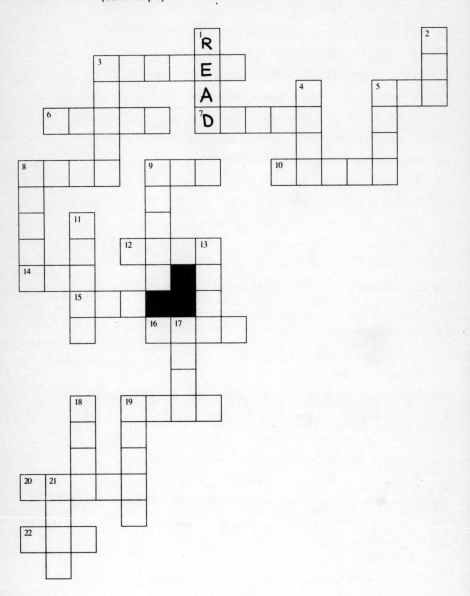

Across →

3 You .... to the radio. (6)

5 You .... things with a knife. (3)

6 My brother is only two but he can already .... from 1 to 100. (5)

7 You .... a car. (5)

8 You .... your hands when they are dirty. (4)

9 After you wash your hands, you .... them with a towel. (3)

10 I usually .... coffee in the morning. (5)

12 You should always .... on the pavement. (4)

14 Animals only .... food when they are hungry. (3)

15 People often .... when they are sad. (3)

16 I went to the post office to .... a letter. (4)

19 Can you .... a song in French? (4)

20 My cousin can .... two languages. (5)

22 You should always .... your electricity bill on time. (3)

Down ↓

1 I .... a newspaper every day. (4)

2 She told us to .... on the sofa. (3)

3 I always .... when I see Charlie Chaplin films. They are so funny! (5)

4 The men in this office always .... suits. (4)

5 I was hungry so I decided to .... a meal. (4)

8 You .... with a pen or a pencil. (5)

9 You usually .... at night when you are asleep. (5)

11 How often do you .... television? (5)

13 She asked me to .... her on the lips. (4)

17 Could you .... the window, please? It's very hot in here. (4)

18 Do you know how to .... a horse? (4)

19 I used to .... forty cigarettes a day. (5)

21 Would you like to .... tennis on Saturday? (4)

Picture crossword: clothes

Look at the drawings and complete the crossword.

Across →

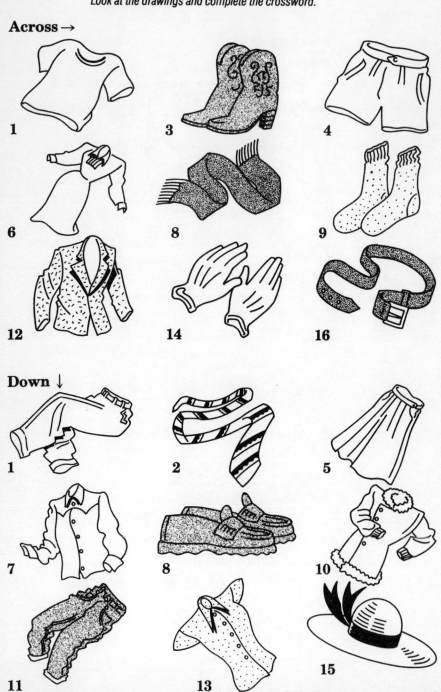

1

3

4

6

8

9

12

14

16

Down ↓

1

2

5

7

8

10

11

13

15

16 Singular and plural

Complete the crossword by filling in the missing words in the table (singular or plural noun). (See example)

Across →

Singular	Plural
2 Across (5)	children
baby	3 Across (6)
tomato	6 Across (8)
foot	7 Across (4)
8 Across (6)	cheeses
city	11 Across (6)
watch	12 Across (7)
knife	13 Across (6)
15 Across (7)	factories
glass	16 Across (7)

Down ↓

Singular	Plural
flower	1 Down (7)
car	2 Down (4)
box	4 Down (5)
5 Down (3)	men
tooth	6 Down (5)
mouse	9 Down (4)
10 Down (3)	buses
12 Down (5)	women
14 Down (5)	geese
17 Down (4)	ladies

17 Where did I go?

Read the sentences and complete the crossword. Each of the missing words is a place or a building.

Across →

4 I went to the .... to have a meal. (10)

5 I went to the .... to meet my cousin who was flying here from New York. (7)

8 I went to the ....'s to buy some flowers. (7)

9 I went to the .... to post a parcel. (4,6)

10 I went to the .... to have my car repaired. (6)

11 I went to the .... to see the tigers, lions, elephants, monkeys, etc. (3)

12 I went to the Grand .... to meet some friends who were staying there for the weekend. (5)

13 I went to the .... to talk to my son's teachers. (6)

16 I went to the ....'s to buy some fruit and vegetables. (11)

18 I went to the .... for a haircut and a shave. (6)

20 I went to the .... to buy food for the weekend. (11)

Down ↓

1 I went to the .... to book a holiday to Majorca. (6,6)

2 I went to the .... to cash a cheque. (4)

3 I went to the .... to catch a train. (7)

6 I went to the .... to buy a pair of slippers. (4,4)

7 I went to the .... when I broke my arm. (8)

14 I went to the .... to borrow some books. (7)

15 I went to the ....'s to buy a ring for my wife. (8)

17 I went to the .... to see the new James Bond film. (6)

18 I went to the .... to swim and sunbathe. (5)

19 I went to the .... to have a drink with friends. (3)

18 Classifications

*Peter, David, John are all **names**. Monday, Wednesday, Friday are all **days**. Complete the crossword by finding one word to classify each of the groups of three words. To help you, the answers are given but the letters are mixed up. (See example)*

Across →

3   23, 99, 15 (MUNBRES) (7)

5   Wales, Italy, Spain (SINUCEROT) (9)

6   rose, tulip, crocus (WFLOSER) (7)

7   uncle, cousin, aunt (EASTLVIRE) (9)

9   New York, London, Tokyo (SCIETI) (6)

10   fly, ant, bee (NISETCS) (7)

13   milk, beer, wine (RISDNK) (6)

16   football, tennis, golf (SORPST) (6)

17   church, school, hotel (BUDSLIGNI) (9)

18   apples, bananas, oranges (RUFIT) (5)

20   spaniel, poodle, terrier (GODS) (4)

21   carrots, peas, potatoes (TABSLEEVEG) (10)

Down ↓

1   table, sofa, chair (FEUTIRUNR) (9)

2   A, C, W (TETELRS) (7)

4   sparrow, pigeon, eagle (SDIRB) (5)

8   lion, horse, elephant (INASALM) (7)

11   spring, summer, winter (NOSSEAS) (7)

12   orange, green, blue (CRUSLOO) (7)

14   April, July, November (TOMSNH) (6)

15   trousers, shirt, dress (SOLCHET) (7)

19   snow, rain, fog (HEWRETA) (7)

20   waltz, samba, cha-cha (NEDSAC) (6)

22   hammer, saw, screwdriver (SOLTO) (5)

Missing words

Read the text and fill in the missing words in the crossword.

Hello. My ....(18 Across) is Colin Moon. I am forty-two ....(5 Across) old. I am married. My ....(12 Down) is called Kathleen. ....(23 Across) is two years younger ....(3 Down) me and comes from Ireland.

We ....(13 Across) in a town called Milton Keynes, ...(11 Across) is about 40 miles north-west of London. We have two ....(6 Across) – Peter and Susan. Peter ....(22 Across) fifteen and Susan is twelve. We also ....(8 Down) a cat called Zorro ....(7 Across) a goldfish called Wanda.

I am a teacher and Kathleen ....(20 Across) in a bank. She always drives to work but I usually go ....(17 Across) bus. ....(16 Down) is a bus stop just outside our house.

We don't go out very often in the evenings – we ....(10 Down) stay at home and watch ....(1 Down) or ....(15 Across) to music. We sometimes drive into the country ....(7 Down) the weekend or go to the ....(14 Across) – we saw the latest James Bond film two weeks ....(19 Down). It was really good!

We have lived in Milton Keynes ....(21 Down) 1986. We moved here ....(2 Down) Liverpool. We like the town, ...(9 Across) one day we ....(20 Down) like to move to the south coast – possibly to Hastings ....(4 Down) to Brighton.

20 5-letter words

In this crossword, each of the missing words has five letters. The first and last letter of each word is given, with a clue. (See example)

Across →

3 R___D A ball is this shape.

6 S___P A farm animal.

8 G___N A colour.

10 F___T e.g. pears, apples, bananas.

11 C___K Something you look at when you want to know what the time is.

13 E___T A country in north Africa.

15 A___E Higher than; over.

18 T___R A wild animal found in India.

19 S___T Something a man wears.

20 Y___G Not old.

23 H___E You live in it.

24 D___S Something a woman wears.

Down ↓

1 L__H From Ireland.

2 Q___N The wife of a King.

4 F___T The opposite of last.

5 S___P You do it at night.

7 P___E You keep money in it – usually coins.

9 F___E A musical instrument; you blow it.

12 C___N Not dirty.

14 T___E A piece of furniture.

16 M___H A month.

17 F___Y A number.

19 S___R It tastes sweet; people often put it in tea and coffee.

21 G___S What bottles are made of.

22 C___R You sit on it.

21 What's the word? 2

Read the sentences, decide what 'it' is used instead of, and complete the crossword. (See example)

Across →

5   I put a stamp on it before I posted the letter. (8)

7   I was feeling very tired, so I lay down on it and went to sleep. (3)

8   It shows you are married. You wear it on your finger. (4)

9   It fell during the night and in the morning all the fields and streets were white. (4)

12   Everyone knew it and sang along loudly. (4)

13   I usually switch it on and listen to music programmes while I drive. (5)

14   Stefan Edberg lost the match when he hit it into the net. (4)

16   She had lost it, so she couldn't open the door of her flat. (3)

17   It wasn't working, so I had to use the stairs to visit my cousin who lived on the ninth floor. (4)

20   I packed everything in it the night before I went on holiday. (8)

21   He took very nice photographs of the Christmas party with it. (6)

23   Don't be afraid; it won't bite. It barks a lot but it's a very friendly animal really. (3)

24   We ordered a bottle of it with our meal. We chose red as we were eating meat. (4)

25   It was late. When it finally arrived there were more than twenty people waiting at the stop. (3)

Down ↓

1   It rang three times before he answered it. (9)

2   I borrowed it from him to write my name. (3)

3   Our teacher gives us lots of it. It usually takes me one or two hours to do it every evening. (8)

4   I usually drink it when I go to the pub. I prefer it to wine or whisky. (4)

6   It was very strong and blew my hat off while I was walking down the street. (4)

10   He put it out when he saw the No Smoking sign on the wall. (9)

11   It wasn't very big – just one room, a kitchen and a bathroom. But the rent was cheap and it wasn't too far from where she worked. (4)

15   It flew from Heathrow airport to Copenhagen. (5)

18   It was directed by Stephen Spielberg and starred Dustin Hoffman and Meryl Streep. (4)

19   I bought it in Spain. It's the national instrument there. But I wish I could play flamenco music like them. (6)

22   I gave it to her so she could visit me if she ever came to Brighton. (7)

22 Picture crossword: things in the home

Look at the drawings and complete the crossword.

Across →

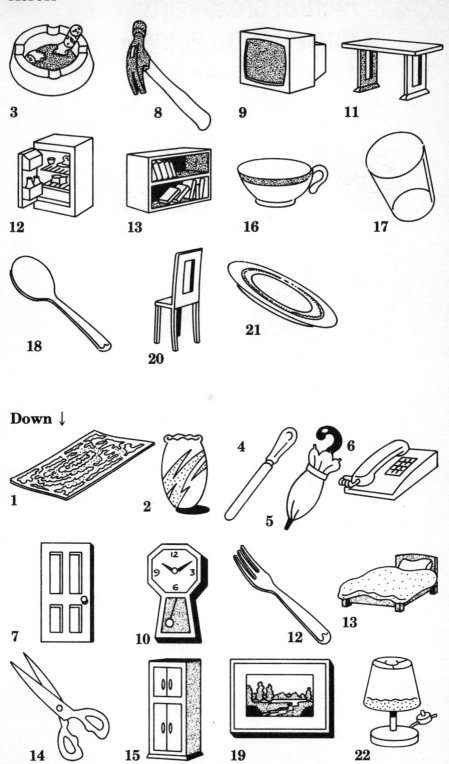

3

8

9

11

12

13

16

17

18

20

21

Down ↓

1

2

4

5

6

7

10

12

13

14

15

19

22

23 A letter

Maria comes from Italy. She has come to England for the summer to learn English. She is staying with a family in Hastings and she goes to school there every day. This is a letter she wrote for homework. Complete the crossword by filling in the missing words in the letter.

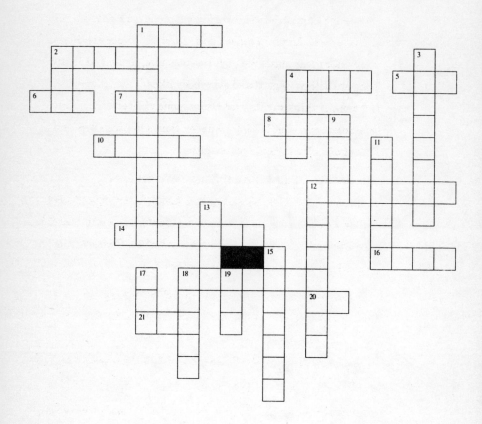

Dear Julia,

I'm having a wonderful ....(13 Down) here in Hastings. The ....(18 Across) is lovely (sunshine nearly every day) and the family I'm staying with – Mr ....(19 Down) Mrs Harris – are really friendly. They ....(9 Down) a fifteen-year-old ....(3 Down) called Pamela. We have become good friends and spend a lot ....(20 Across) time together.

The house I'm staying in is quite big. It ....(5 Across) a kitchen, a dining-room, a living-room, a ....(12 Down) (with a very big bath!) and four bedrooms. My bedroom is very

nice and ....(15 Down) my window you can ....
(2 Down) the sea. There is also a large garden with seven apple
trees and two pear trees. Pamela and I sometimes ....
(4 Across) badminton on the lawn, but I'm ....(17 Down)
very good at it, so Pamela ....(11 Down) wins.

We have English lessons every day (Monday–Friday)
.....................(12 Across) 9 o'clock and 12 o'clock. There are fifteen
altogether in my class. We have two teachers, Brian and Jenny.
They are both very good and everybody likes ....
(1 Across). I think my English has got much better ....
(2 Across) I came to Hastings. I understand a lot more now and
I'm not afraid to speak to people either.

In the afternoons we sometimes go to the beach or
.....................(21 Across) park or go and visit different places. Last
Friday we all ....(7 Across) to Brighton. I loved it there!
There was so ....(8 Across) to see and do. Perhaps next
year I'll choose a language holiday in Brighton.

In the evenings we usually go to the school's own disco.
Sometimes I go out with Pamela to the cinema or to visit
.....................(6 Across) friends. I also stay at home and watch
.....................(1 Down) with Mr and Mrs Harris. (It's a good way to
learn ....(14 Across) too!)

On Saturday we're ....(10 Across) to London for the day.
It should be fun! We're going to visit Madame Tussaud's, St.
.....................'s (4 Down) Cathedral and the Tower of London. I hope
we have time after that to go shopping in Oxford Street. I want to
buy ....(16 Across) presents to take home with me.

Well, Julia, that's all I have to say for now, but I hope to see you
when I get home again. Only two ....(18 Down) left now!

Love,

Maria

24 Mixed up clues

In this crossword, all the words have been filled in, but the clues are all mixed up. Write the correct answer (1 Down, 2 Across, etc.) in front of each clue. (See example)

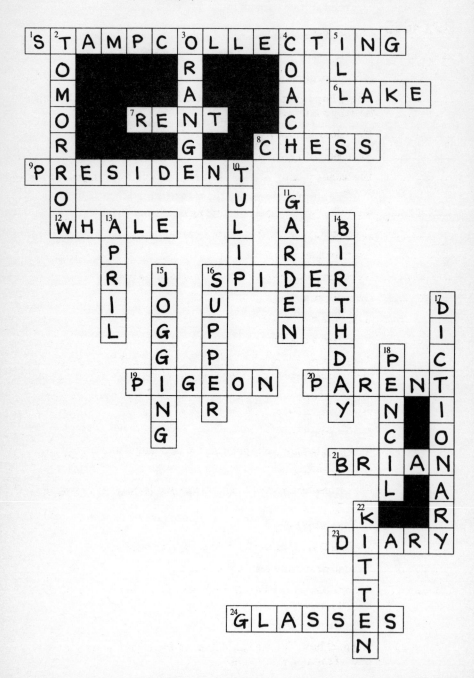

Across →
Down ↓

9 ACROSS
.... The head of a republic.

.... A young cat.

.... A common spring flower.

.... A very large animal that lives in the sea. It looks like a fish but it is really a mammal.

.... The colour you get when you mix red and yellow.

.... An insect with eight legs.

.... The money you pay each week or each month to live in your flat or house.

.... A popular hobby, especially among teenagers.

.... Everyone has one of these once a year.

.... The fourth month of the year.

.... Something people wear to help them to see better.

.... Not well; sick.

.... A boy's name.

.... A mother or a father.

.... A very large area of water surrounded by land. There are five famous ones between Canada and the USA.

.... Many houses have one of these. People often plant flowers, fruit or vegetables in them or they are covered with grass.

.... A type of bus.

.... A popular way of getting exercise. It is running slowly – usually without getting too tired.

.... A book in which you can write down what happens to you every day.

.... The day after today.

.... You use this if you want to find out what a word means.

.... A meal eaten quite late in the evening.

.... A game played on a board with black and white squares. Russians are very good at it.

.... You can write or draw with it.

.... A type of bird. You see lots of them in Trafalgar Square and in most of the squares in Venice.

25 What's the word? 3

Complete the crossword by reading the clues. The letters of each word are
given but they are mixed up.

Across →

3   One of the rooms of a house. (TIKENHC) (7)
5   A capital city in the north of Europe. (ONCAHENGEP) (10)
7   He can't hear; he's .... (FEAD) (4)
8   In a house, smoke comes out of this. (CHENYIM) (7)
9   Saturday and Sunday. (KEENWED) (7)
12 e.g. 'Cats', 'The Sound of Music' and 'Phantom of the Opera'. (CASLIUM) (7)
13 You buy one of these when you travel by bus, by train or when you go to the theatre. It shows you have paid for your seat. (EKITCT) (6)
14 Men sometimes smoke one of these after a meal. The best ones come from Havana. (IRACG) (5)
16 You usually use this when you eat soup or a dessert. (SONOP) (5)
18 People use this when it is raining. It stops you getting wet. (ARELLBUM) (8)
19 e.g. Jones, Smith, Wilson or Kennedy. (ARNEUMS) (7)
21 We get milk from this animal. (WOC) (3)
22 He went into the shop and bought a .... of biscuits. (ATEKCP) (6)
24 A meal in the middle of the day. (CLUHN) (5)
26 This person flies an aeroplane. (TOLIP) (5)
27 The highest one in the world is called Everest. (AMTONNUI) (8)
28 One of the languages of Switzerland. (ERHCNF) (6)

Down ↓

1   A musical instrument. (ONPIA) (5)
2   A place where you can study after you have left school. (SNUVETIRIY) (10)
4   Your mother's brother's child. (SINCOU) (6)
6   Fruit. You make wine from these. (SAPERG) (6)
8   A very special festival in December for Christians. People usually send cards and buy presents for each other. (SATHRISCM) (9)
10 Harrods is a very large and famous .... store in London. (MARNEDTEPT) (10)
11 Seven days. (EWEK) (4)
12 It shines at night. (NOMO) (4)
15 A popular sport – especially in Scotland, Japan and the USA. Severiano Ballesteros plays it. (FOGL) (4)
17 People wear one of these to know what the time is. (CHWAT) (5)
20 One of the planets. (JETIRUP) (7)
23 One of the seasons. (MUUTAN) (6)
25 You can kill someone with this. (UGN) (3)

Answers

1 Numbers

Across
2 sixty-three 6 seven 8 five 10 eight 11 tenth 13 four
14 fifteen 16 twelve 20 fourteen
Down
1 fifth 3 thirteen 4 eleven 5 hundred 7 sixteen 9 thousand
12 thirty 15 twenty 17 eighteen 18 twentieth 19 three

2 Picture crossword: food and drink

Across
3 beer 4 oranges 6 apples 8 tea 9 water 10 cheese
11 fish 12 cakes 13 biscuits 15 pears 16 wine 17 meat
Down
1 potatoes 2 eggs 3 bread 5 sausages 7 banana
10 coffee 12 chicken 14 tomatoes

3 Opposites: adjectives

Across
1 cheap 7 alive 9 poor 10 ugly 11 dirty 13 wet
14 easy 16 wrong 19 small 21 old 22 slow 23 thick
Down
2 happy 3 early 4 kind 5 light 6 cold 8 empty 12 thin
15 soft 16 weak 17 good 18 closed 19 short 20 low

4 Irregular verbs 1

Across
2 brought 5 break 6 taught 8 spoke 10 carried 12 met
14 heard 15 sold 17 got 18 see
Down
1 bought 3 write 4 was 7 thought 8 sat 9 said 11 did
13 fall 15 slept 16 lost

5 Which country is it?

Across
3 Saudi Arabia 5 Holland 7 Canada 9 Russia 12 Spain
13 Poland 15 Germany 16 Kenya 17 Mexico
Down
1 Wales 2 Finland 3 Switzerland 4 Monaco 6 Japan
8 New Zealand 10 Italy 11 India 12 Sweden 14 Brazil
15 Greece

6 Dialogues

Across

3 old   4 Which   5 please   10 thanks   12 Hello   13 far
14 Where   15 does   17 sorry   18 When

Down

1 Excuse   2 Congratulations   6 luck   7 What   8 tall
9 younger   11 size   12 Have   16 morning   18 Whose

7 Prepositions

Across

3 outside   6 in front of   9 between   14 through   15 corner

Down

1 inside   2 on   4 under   5 in   7 opposite   8 over   10 next to
11 behind   12 right   13 from

8 Picture crossword: parts of the body

Across

1 cheek   4 lip   5 nose   6 toe   8 neck   10 foot   11 arm
13 chin   15 ear   16 elbow   17 head

Down

2 eye   3 knee   4 leg   6 tongue   7 tooth   9 hair   10 finger
12 mouth   14 hand

9 What's the job?

Across

3 baker   6 doctor   7 gardener   9 actress   10 carpenter
13 teacher   14 artist   17 journalist   19 shop assistant

Down

1 sailor   2 window cleaner   4 chef   5 fireman   8 librarian
10 car mechanic   11 policeman   12 dentist   15 optician
16 postman   18 nurse

10 Opposites: verbs

Across

1 start   2 close   4 lose   6 forget   9 push   12 learn
13 answer   15 die

Down

1 sell   2 come   3 cry   5 shout   6 finish   7 take   8 win
10 hate   11 lend   14 leave

11 A family tree

Across

3 grandchildren   5 son   8 wife   9 parents   11 father
14 uncle   15 sister   16 nephew

Down
1 daughter   2 brother   4 husband   6 children   7 mother
10 cousin   12 aunt   13 niece

12   Irregular verbs 2

Across
1 sang   2 build   4 run   6 gave   7 broke   8 freeze   9 caught
12 took   13 flew   16 went   17 cut
Down
1 swim   2 bit   3 drank   5 understood   7 become   10 hide
11 make   14 left   15 kept

13   What's the word? 1

Across
2 coal   3 stamp   5 map   8 head   9 flour   11 house
13 brown   15 eight   17 late   18 pound   20 coffee   21 snow
Down
1 fat   2 comb   4 tea   5 Mars   6 peach   7 chair
9 friend   10 egg   12 shave   13 book   14 wood   16 west
19 sun   20 cow

14   Which verb?

Across
3 listen   5 cut   6 count   7 drive   8 wash   9 dry   10 drink
12 walk   14 eat   15 cry   16 post   19 sing   20 speak   22 pay
Down
1 read   2 sit   3 laugh   4 wear   5 cook   8 write
9 dream   11 watch   13 kiss   17 open   18 ride   19 smoke
21 play

15   Picture crossword: clothes

Across
1 T-shirt   3 boots   4 shorts   6 dress   8 scarf   9 socks
12 jacket   14 gloves   16 belt
Down
1 trousers   2 tie   5 skirt   7 shirt   8 shoes   10 coat
11 jeans   13 blouse   15 hat

16   Singular and plural

Across
2 child   3 babies   6 tomatoes   7 feet   8 cheese   11 cities
12 watches   13 knives   15 factory   16 glasses
Down
1 flowers   2 cars   4 boxes   5 man   6 teeth   9 mice   10 bus
12 woman   14 goose   17 lady

17 Where did I go?

Across

4 restaurant   5 airport   8 florist   9 post office   10 garage
11 zoo   12 Hotel   13 school   16 greengrocer   18 barber
20 supermarket

Down

1 travel agency   2 bank   3 station   6 shoe shop   7 hospital
14 library   15 jeweller   17 cinema   18 beach   19 pub

18 Classifications

Across

3 numbers   5 countries   6 flowers   7 relatives   9 cities
10 insects   13 drinks   16 sports   17 buildings   18 fruit
20 dogs   21 vegetables

Down

1 furniture   2 letters   4 birds   8 animals   11 seasons
12 colours   14 months   15 clothes   19 weather   20 dances
22 tools

19 Missing words

Across

5 years   6 children   7 and   9 but   11 which   13 live
14 cinema   15 listen   17 by   18 name   20 works   22 is
23 She

Down

1 television   2 from   3 than   4 or   7 at   8 have   10 usually
12 wife   16 There   19 ago   20 would   21 since

20 5-letter words

Across

3 round   6 sheep   8 green   10 fruit   11 clock   13 Egypt
15 above   18 tiger   19 shirt   20 young   23 house   24 dress

Down

1 Irish   2 queen   4 first   5 sleep   7 purse   9 flute   12 clean
14 table   16 March   17 fifty   19 sugar   21 glass   22 chair

21 What's the word? 2

Across

5 envelope   7 bed   8 ring   9 snow   12 song   13 radio
14 ball   16 key   17 lift   20 suitcase   21 camera   23 dog
24 wine   25 bus

Down

1 telephone   2 pen   3 homework   4 beer   6 wind   10 cigarette
11 flat   15 plane   18 film   19 guitar   22 address

22 Picture crossword: things in the home

Across
3 ashtray 8 hammer 9 television 11 table 12 fridge
13 bookcase 16 cup 17 glass 18 spoon 20 chair 21 plate
Down
1 carpet 2 vase 4 knife 5 umbrella 6 telephone 7 door
10 clock 12 fork 13 bed 14 scissors 15 cupboard
19 painting 22 lamp

23 A letter

Across
1 them 2 since 4 play 5 has 6 her 7 went 8 much
10 going 12 between 14 English 16 some 18 weather
20 of 21 the
Down
1 television 2 see 3 daughter 4 Paul 9 have 11 always
12 bathroom 13 time 15 through 17 not 18 weeks 19 and

24 Mixed up clues

9 Across   The head of a republic.
22 Down   A young cat.
10 Down   A common spring flower.
12 Across   A very large animal ...
3 Down   The colour you get ...
16 Across   An insect with eight legs.
7 Across   The money you pay each week ...
1 Across   A popular hobby ...
14 Down   Everyone has one of these once a year.
13 Down   The fourth month of the year.
24 Across   Something people wear ...
5 Down   Not well; sick.
21 Across   A boy's name.
20 Across   A mother or a father.
6 Across   A very large area of water ...
11 Down   Many houses have one of these ...
4 Down   A type of bus.
15 Down   A popular way of getting exercise ...
23 Across   A book in which you can write ...
2 Down   The day after today.
17 Down   You use this if you want to find out ...
16 Down   A meal eaten quite late in the evening.
8 Across   A game played on a board ...
18 Down   You can write or draw with it.
19 Across   A type of bird ...

25 What's the word? 3

Across

3 kitchen   5 Copenhagen   7 deaf   8 chimney   9 weekend
12 musical   13 ticket   14 cigar   16 spoon   18 umbrella
19 surname   21 cow   22 packet   24 lunch   26 pilot
27 mountain   28 French

Down

1 piano   2 university   4 cousin   6 grapes   8 Christmas
10 department   11 week   12 moon   15 golf   17 watch
20 Jupiter   23 autumn   25 gun

Key words

The number after each word is the crossword in which the word first appeared.
(*v=verb, n=noun, a=adjective*)

above 20
actress 9
address 21
ago 19
airport 17
alive 3
always 23
and 19
animals 18
answer (v) 10
apples 2
April 24
arm 8
artist 9
ashtray 22
at 19
at the corner of 7
aunt 11
autumn 25

babies 16
baker 9
ball 21
banana 2
bank 17
barber 17
bathroom 23
beach 17
become 12
bed 21
beer 2
behind 7
belt 15
between 7
birds 18
birthday 24
biscuits 2
bit (v) 12
blouse 15
book 13
bookcase 22
boots 15
bought 4
boxes 16
Brazil 5
bread 2
break 4

Brian 24
broke 12
brother 11
brought 4
brown 13
build 12
buildings 18
bus 16
but 19
by 19

cakes 2
camera 21
Canada 5
car mechanic 9
carpenter 9
carpet 22
carried 4
cars 16
caught 12
chair 13
cheap 3
cheek 8
cheese 2
chef 9
chess 24
chicken 2
child 16
children 11
chimney 25
chin 8
Christmas 25
cigar 25
cigarette 21
cinema 17
cities 16
clean (a) 20
clock 20
close (v) 10
closed 3
clothes 18
coach 24
coal 13
coat 15
coffee 2
cold 3
colours 18

comb 13
come 10
congratulations 6
cook (v) 14
Copenhagen 25
corner 7
count 14
countries 18
cousin 11
cow 13
cry 10
cup 22
cupboard 22
cut (v) 12

dances (n) 18
daughter 11
deaf 25
dentist 9
department 25
diary 24
dictionary 24
did 4
die 10
dirty 3
doctor 9
does 6
dog 21
dogs 18
door 22
drank 12
dream (v) 14
dress (n) 15
drink (v) 14
drinks (n) 18
drive 14
dry (v) 14

ear 8
early 3
easy 3
eat 14
egg 13
eggs 2
Egypt 20
eight 1
eighteen 1

elbow 8
eleven 1
empty 3
English 23
envelope 21
excuse 6
eye 8

factory 16
fall 4
far 6
fat 13
father 11
feet 16
fifteen 1
fifth 1
fifty 20
film 21
finger 8
finish 10
Finland 5
fireman 9
first 20
fish 2
five 1
flat (n) 21
flew 12
florist 17
flour 13
flowers 16
flute 20
foot 8
forget 10
fork 22
four 1
fourteen 1
freeze 12
French 25
fridge 22
friend 13
from 7
fruit 18
furniture 18

garage 17
garden 24
gardener 9

gave 12
Germany 5
glass 20
glasses 16
glasses (=spectacles) 23
gloves 15
going 23
golf 25
good 3
goose 16
got 4
grandchildren 11
grapes 25
Greece 5
green 20
greengrocer 17
guitar 21
gun 25

hair 8
hammer 22
hand 8
happy 3
has 23
hat 15
hate 10
have 6
head 8
heard 4
hello 6
her 23
hide 12
Holland 5
homework 21
hospital 17
hotel 17
house 13
hundred 1
husband 11

ill 24
in 7
in front of 7
India 5
insects 18
inside 7
Irish 20
is 19
Italy 5

jacket 15
Japan 5
jeans 15

jeweller 17
jogging 24
journalist 9
Jupiter 25

Kenya 5
kept 12
key 21
kind (a) 3
kiss (v) 14
kitchen 25
kitten 24
knee 8
knife 22
knives 16

lady 16
lake 24
lamp 22
late 13
laugh (v) 14
learn 10
leave 10
left (v) 12
leg 8
lend 10
letters 18
librarian 9
library 17
lift (n) 21
light (a) 3
lip 8
listen 14
live (v) 19
lose 10
lost (v) 4
low 3
luck 6
lunch 25

make 12
man 16
map 13
March 20
Mars 13
meat 2
met 4
Mexico 5
mice 16
Monaco 5
months 18
moon 25
morning 6

mother 11
mountain 25
mouth 8
much 23
musical 25

name 19
neck 8
nephew 11
New Zealand 5
next to 7
niece 11
nose 8
not 23
numbers 18
nurse 9

of 23
old 3
on 7
on the right 7
open (v) 14
opposite 7
optician 9
or 19
orange (a) 24
oranges 2
outside 7
over 7

packet 25
painting 22
parent 24
parents 11
Paul 23
pay 14
peach 13
pears 2
pen 21
pencil 24
piano 25
pigeon 24
pilot 25
plane 21
plate 22
play (v) 14
please 6
Poland 5
policeman 9
poor 3
post (v) 14
post office 17
postman 9

potatoes 2
pound 13
president 24
pub 17
purse 20
push 10

queen 20

radio 21
read 14
relatives 18
rent (n) 24
restaurant 17
ride 14
right 7
ring (n) 21
round 20
run 12
Russia 5

said 4
sailor 9
sang 12
sat 4
Saudi Arabia 5
sausages 2
scarf 15
school 17
scissors 22
seasons 18
see 4
sell 10
seven 1
shave 13
she 19
sheep 20
shirt 15
shoe shop 17
shoes 15
shop assistant 9
short 3
shorts 15
shout 10
since 19
sing 14
sister 11
sit 14
sixteen 1
sixty-three 1
size 6
skirt 15
sleep (v) 20

slept 4
slow 3
small 3
smoke (v) 14
snow 13
socks 15
soft 3
sold 4
some 23
son 11
song 21
sorry 6
Spain 5
speak 14
spider 24
spoke 4
spoon 22
sports 18
St Paul's cathedral 23
stamp (n) 13
stamp collecting 24
start (v) 10
station 17
sugar 20
suitcase 21
sun 13
supermarket 17
supper 24
surname 25
Sweden 5
swim 12
Switzerland 5

table 20
take 10
tall 6
taught 4
tea 2
teacher 9
teeth 16
telephone 21
television 19
tenth 1
than 19
thanks 6
the 23
them 23
there 19
thick 3
thin 3
thirteen 1
thirty 1
thought 4
thousand 1
three 1
through 7
ticket 25
tie (n) 15
tiger 20
time 23
toe 8
tomatoes 2
tomorrow 24
tongue 8
took 12

tools 18
tooth 8
travel agency 17
trousers 15
T-shirt 15
tulip 24
twelve 1
twentieth 1
twenty 1

ugly 3
umbrella 22
uncle 11
under 7
understood 12
university 25
usually 19

vase 22
vegetables 18

Wales 5
walk 14
was 4
wash 14
watch (v) 14
watch (n) 25
watches (n) 16
water 2
weak 3
wear 14
weather 18

week 25
weekend 25
weeks 23
went 12
west 13
wet 3
whale 24
what 6
when 6
where 6
which 6
whose 6
wife 11
win 10
wind 21
window cleaner 9
wine 2
woman 16
wood 13
works (v) 19
would 19
write 4
wrong 3

years 19
young 20
younger 6

zoo 17